B85

A TOKEN
FOR FRIENDS

being
A Memoir of Edgar Osborne

An Appreciation of
The Osborne Collection
of Early Children's Books

and
A Facsimile of His Catalogue
'From Morality & Instruction
to Beatrix Potter'

1979

Edgar Osborne, MA, LLD, FLA
1890-1978

EDGAR OSBORNE WAS A DISTINGUISHED LIBRARIAN, A wise administrator, an erudite scholar, a discerning book-man, a shrewd and knowledgeable collector, and a country-man who loved the out of doors. This man of vision and amazing generosity was unassuming and kindly in manner and endowed with a lively sense of humour. Along with his literary pursuits and professional career as County Librarian of Derbyshire, England, he took an active part in local af-fairs, serving on the Council of the Derbyshire Archaeologi-cal and Natural History Society, on the Diocesan Committee for the Care of Churches, and on the executive committee of the Derbyshire Rural Community Council from its forma-tion in 1924. He edited the *Derbyshire Countryside* from 1944 to 1955.

Mr. Osborne became interested in children's books at an early age. He was born on 23 March 1890 in Christchurch, near Bournemouth. His father, Albert Osborne, was a post-man. His mother was the former Louisa Jane Hall, and it was from her family that Edgar inherited the nursery library that was to form the nucleus of his collection of early children's books. As a boy he attended St. Paul's Church School in Bournemouth. Because the town had no secondary schools at that time and 'education was difficult for poor boys', he spent six years in independent study at home, in the public library, and at evening classes. His education came largely from the books he read. He knew first-hand the potential power and the pleasure that come from wide reading in childhood. He was to become a champion of library services for children and an authority on the books published for them during the last four hundred years.

In World War 1 Mr. Osborne escaped from the horrors of trench warfare by volunteering for active duty in the Middle East where he stayed without furlough for four years. 'It was like living in a Henty book', he once confided. He served under General Allenby and had vivid memories of Christmas eve and Christmas-day, 1917, when he was in charge of the guard at the Holy Manger in Bethlehem. After his return to England, he qualified as a librarian and he married Mabel Jacobson, a Shakespearean actress who was especially interested in the Little Theatre movement and in verse-speaking. Together they began to collect the books that they had known and enjoyed as children. Through the years they gathered a representative collection of children's books, going backwards in time to 1566 when the Plantin Press of Antwerp published an edition of Aesop for schoolboys.

In 1923, after working in the municipal libraries of Bournemouth and Sheffield, Edgar Osborne was appointed the County Librarian of Derbyshire with a staff of two assistants and a stock of twelve thousand books. When he retired in 1954 he left one of the largest and most highly developed county libraries in the United Kingdom. His contribution to librarianship was recognized in 1958 when the University of Nottingham conferred on him an honorary Master of Arts degree.

After attending a conference of the American Library Association in 1934 as a delegate of the Library Association of Great Britain, Mr. Osborne with his wife paid a brief visit to Toronto where they met Miss Lillian H. Smith, the head of the children's library services that she had organized in 1912. They were both deeply impressed by Boys and Girls House, already a unique centre for the study of children's literature, and by the network of children's libraries throughout the Toronto Public Library system. It was after this visit that Mrs. Osborne suggested that sometime their collection of children's books might find its permanent home in Toronto.

Mabel Osborne died in 1946. The following year Mr. Osborne wrote to Dr. Charles R. Sanderson, the Chief Librarian, offering to give his books to the Toronto Public Library as a tribute to Miss Smith and as a memorial of his wife, on condition that the collection be augmented, maintained as a unit, housed adequately and accessibly, and that it be staffed by a children's librarian. He stipulated that a printed catalogue should be published within a reasonable length of time. The Osborne Collection of Early Children's Books was officially presented at a ceremony in the Eaton Auditorium on 14 November 1949 in the presence of the Lieutenant-Governor of Ontario who opened the exhibition that had been previously mounted in the Towner Art Gallery, Eastbourne, before the books left England. These books are again being exhibited in 1979 in the Osborne Room of Boys and Girls House as a memorial of the donor and as a symbol of gratitude for his gift presented thirty years ago.

Mr. Osborne was only fifty-eight years old when he generously parted with the books he intimately knew and loved. Had he waited to leave them as a bequest, no institution at the present time could assemble a collection of the size and significance of the Osborne Collection which now holds nearly twelve thousand items.

Under the guidance of Miss Jean Thomson (Miss Smith's successor) and Dr. Sanderson, who had been trained in bibliography in England, the catalogue began to take form. About half the books were catalogued when Dr. Sanderson suddenly became ill and died. At the suggestion of his successor, Henry C. Campbell, the Library Board retained the services of Mr. Osborne as an adviser in the autumn of 1956. He worked at Boys and Girls House for five weeks, resolving baffling problems and helping to make final decisions about the publication. He thoroughly enjoyed these few weeks when many lasting friendships were formed with members of the staff.

After his return to England, he married, in April 1957, Kerstin Munck af Rosenschöld, a Swedish librarian, who was until her retirement the City Librarian of Lund. Mr. and Mrs. Osborne visited Toronto in May 1959 to celebrate the mid-winter publication of the Osborne Catalogue and again in 1965 when a memorable colloquium was arranged in their honour. Fourteen book-collectors were invited by the Board to come to Toronto to meet Mr. and Mrs. Osborne and to share mutual enthusiasms and knowledge. At the final session, the plan to organize a 'Friends of the Osborne and Lillian H. Smith Collections' was announced.

After his retirement in 1954 Mr. Osborne served as the first professional librarian to the Marquess of Salisbury at Hatfield House. He was later the private librarian to the FitzRoy Newdegate family at Arbury Hall. During these years, however, he was never too busy to share his wisdom and experience nor to give counsel and answers to our bibliographical queries. He liked to be informed about activities at Boys and Girls House, acquisitions for the Collection, and news of his friends on the staff. Every year he gave additional items, including such generous gifts as the rare 1549 edition of Hans Holbein's *Images of the Old Testament*, with text in both French and English, and his collection of valentines.

Edgar Osborne's last visit to Toronto was in June, 1970, when the University of Toronto honoured him as a civic benefactor by conferring on him the degree of Doctor of Laws, *honoris causa*, 'to celebrate the prescience of the pioneer, the discoveries of the timeless researcher, the wisdom of a generous donor'.

Dr. Osborne died on 24 November 1978 at his home in Smalley, near Derby.

JUDITH ST. JOHN
Head, Osborne and Lillian H. Smith Collections

The Osborne Collection
An Appreciation

FROM ITS BEGINNINGS MORE THAN FIFTY YEARS AGO,
the Osborne Collection of historical children's books has had
as its focus 'a representative library of bygone' juveniles –
volumes read and re-read by successive generations, including works 'by indifferent and merely competent writers as
well as those whose merit is universally recognized'. The
stories which precede a tale like *Alice's Adventures in Wonderland* (1865) and that influenced its author (if only as a
catalyst) become almost as important as the classic itself.
This approach gives a new life to the past; it identifies a heri-
tage and tradition of writing for the nursery – one which
allows a fuller understanding of social evolution with its
prevalent attitudes toward childhood. It explains why this
collection, entrusted to the Toronto Public Library at Boys
and Girls House back in 1949, holds a unique position as an
international research centre for scholarship.

The books themselves cover the entire gamut of publications in England up to 1910 – the year Edgar Osborne ended
his adolescence and began what one terms manhood. But
due to the universality of juvenile literature, there are some
notable allowances given for texts first published in other
languages. Aside from the usual Greek and Latin versions of
Aesop, there is a 1697 unauthorized reprint of Charles Per-
rault's *Histoires* better known as 'The Tales of Mother Goose',
the 1819-1822 *Kinder- und Haus-Märchen* of the Brothers
Grimm, Carlo Lorenzini's pseudonymous *Avventure di Pi-
nocchio* (1883), and the original Swedish printing of Selma
Lagerlöf's two-volume *Adventures of Nils* (1906-1907). The
terminal date for these holdings is extended to include more
modern titles through the adjuncted Lillian H. Smith Col-

lection, housed under the same roof and honouring the pioneer efforts of the librarian who established children's library services in Toronto and served as Head of the Boys and Girls Division for forty years. This incorporates such first editions as limited signed copies of A.A. Milne's 'Pooh' books (1924-1928), Jean de Brunhoff's *Histoire de Babar* (1931), and J.R.R. Tolkien's *The Hobbit* (1937). A further entity bridging the two major divisions is the Jean Thomson Collection of Original Art which contains several fine drawings by Kate Greenaway and Randolph Caldecott, a volume of stories with drawings by Walter Crane prepared to entertain his own children (1879), the illustrated manuscript of H.G. Wells's *Adventures of Tommy* (1898, published 1929), and an excellent water-colour by Arthur Rackham, reproduced in his 1906 *Peter Pan in Kensington Gardens*, incorporating a self-caricature of the artist. And there is a further separate collection devoted to Canadian juveniles along with children's books relating to Canada or Canadian studies. Working together, these units form an extensive and thorough assemblage of literature for children in English – along with the best obtainable materials relevant in other languages.

In looking through the 1949 exhibition catalogue of Edgar Osborne's library, we must be impressed even today at the quality and scope of the material: early fables and chapbooks, significant works published by Newbery and John Marshall, titles illustrated with fine woodcuts by John and Thomas Bewick, examples of early play-books produced by the Fullers at their Temple of Fancy, Eleanor Mure's 1831 manuscript version of *The Three Bears*, plus imaginative poetry, adventure stories, moralities and instructional aids incorporating everything from robinsonnades to the first privately printed *Peter Rabbit* (1901). This was a time when relatively little was known about the history of children's books, and few people actually cared about their preservation. Mr. Osborne was one of these pioneers, and in his 1949 catalogue he annotated various entries perhaps to justify his life-long commitment; occasionally he mis-dated an early printed work which looked especially primitive, but he always tried to show their inter-relationship in as accurate a context as possible. His care is apparent when he describes Mary Howitt's 1846 *Wonderful Stories for Children* (182) as 'one of the earliest translations into English of Andersen's fairy stories'; in fact, it is the very first English translation, and this point is precisely made when the book was more fully described in the 1958 Toronto catalogue. But few are the flaws of this earlier list while great are its virtues, for the legacy made by Mr. Osborne thirty years ago stands not just as a collection of books but as a vehicle for active research in both social and literary history.

The very fact that this is not an accumulation only of 'high spots' but a living collection in all its variety has made the Toronto Public Library's published catalogue perhaps the most consulted single reference work in the field. Collectors, librarians and booksellers all over the world use it for annotations and frequently check its 40-page directory of children's book publishers (to be substantially expanded with a cumulative revision appended to Volume III). Countless enquiries have been answered by a carefully trained and informative staff of librarians, helping with bibliographical notes or original studies ranging from academic term papers to innumerable trade publications. In fact, it would be difficult to find any scholarly work recently published dealing with historical juveniles which does not acknowledge the assistance of the Toronto Public Library and its staff at the Osborne Collection. Thousands of visitors each year come to Boys and Girls House, some to do research and others just to look nostalgically at the old books; in the past twenty years alone, the guest book records visitors from sixty countries.

With this reprint of Mr. Osborne's original catalogue, we

pay tribute not only to the memory of the man who first made the collection possible but also to the united efforts of Sheila Egoff, Judith St. John, their associates and their successors, who make the collection so viable and accessible a resource.

JUSTIN G. SCHILLER
New York City

CATALOGUE

OF

AN EXHIBITION

OF

BOOKS FOR CHILDREN

Shewing their development during the
Eighteenth and Nineteenth Centuries

Price One Shilling

THE RATIONAL DAME,

OR,

HINTS TOWARDS SUPPLYING

PRATTLE

FOR

CHILDREN.

The SECOND EDITION.

"We cannot see God, for he is invisible; but we can see his Works; and worship him for his Gifts,"

Hymns in Profe for Children.

LONDON:

Printed and Sold by J. MARSHALL and Co. at No. 17, QUEEN-STREET, CHEAPSIDE, and No. 4, ALDERMARY CHURCH-YARD, in BOW-LANE,

To face the Title.

Dodd del

"Thou most delighted when we roved, see
"The whole maid animal creation round
"Alive and happy—"

Royce sc

Thompfon.

TOWNER ART GALLERY
EASTBOURNE

From Morality & Instruction
to Beatrix Potter

AN

EXHIBITION

OF

BOOKS FOR CHILDREN

FROM THE COLLECTION OF

EDGAR OSBORNE, F.L.A.

COUNTY LIBRARIAN OF DERBYSHIRE

HELD

IN CONNECTION WITH THE

ANNUAL CONFERENCE OF THE

LIBRARY ASSOCIATION

23 MAY **1949** 12 JUNE

CONTENTS

	Page
FOREWORD	3
THE EIGHTEENTH CENTURY AND EARLIER	5
MORAL STORIES IN PROSE	7
MORAL STORIES IN VERSE	9
MORE STORY THAN MORAL	10
BOOKS OF FUN AND NONSENSE	11
CUT-OUT FIGURES AND MOVEABLE BOOKS	12
THE ANIMAL STORY	13
BEATRIX POTTER	14
FABLES	15
FAIRY TALES	16
ROBINSON CRUSOE AND ROBINSONNADES	18
ADVENTURE	19
THE SCHOOL STORY	20
SEDATE PERIODICALS	20
SENSATIONAL PERIODICALS	22
COLOURED BOOKS 1800-1840	23
COLOURED BOOKS 1840-1870	23
NOTABLE ILLUSTRATORS IN LINE AND COLOUR	24

Walter Crane - *Kate Greenaway*
Randolph Caldecott

OTHER NOTABLE ILLUSTRATORS	26
BOOKS OF INSTRUCTION	27

Alphabets - Reading, Writing & Arithmetic
Primary Instruction - *Religious Instruction*
Laws & Constitution - *Natural Science*
Gardening - Trade & Commerce - England &
Other Countries - *History* - *Biography*

FOREWORD

BY

Her Grace The Duchess of Devonshire

THE present exhibition of children's books is primarily due to a suggestion made to me by a few residents in Eastbourne who are interested in the subject of books that have been prepared for children during the past two hundred years or so.

The exhibition would not have been possible without the kind co-operation of the Eastbourne Art Gallery and their curator, Mr. John Lake, of the Library Association, and of Mr. Edgar Osborne, the County Librarian of Derbyshire, who, over the past twenty years, has gathered together a large collection of children's books with the object of illustrating the development of this particular and important type of literature.

It is fortunate that it has been made possible to arrange the opening of the exhibition to coincide with the annual Conference of the Library Association. We are also fortunate in being able to see the books now as this happens to be the first—and I regret to say, the last—time they will be exhibited to the general public in England. To the regret of many of us in Britain, but no doubt to the joy of some of our literary friends in Canada, these books shortly begin their journey overseas. The whole of Mr. Osborne's collection of children's books, of which those mentioned in this catalogue form only a small part, has been given to the Toronto Public Libraries Board. On the arrival of the collection in Canada the books will form a special collection of children's literature to be made available to students specialising in library work with children, and to any other students of literature interested in this most absorbing and entertaining subject.

From this wide range of children's books Mr. Osborne has selected enough typical examples to show their gradual evolution, from the time when writers felt it desirable to point out to children that disaster was always the reward of naughtiness, to the beginning of the twentieth century when they administered their moral lessons in a manner more fitting to our ideas as to how children should behave.

Although Mr. Osborne has entitled his catalogue "From Morality and Instruction to Beatrix Potter", a title which fully indicates the range of the exhibition, a little note of warning is, I feel, necessary. It is true that morality and instruction marched with unrelenting strides across the nurseries of our ancestors; nevertheless, we ought to be mindful of the period in which so many of these books were written and judge the authors of them against the social background of their times. This, I need hardly mention, was vastly different from that with which we are intimate.

One hundred and fifty years ago the adult's approach to the education of children through reading was very different from the present day approach. The philosophy of those days gave writers and parents the impression that children listened with pleasure to what was termed "Rational Information" and that fairy tales and adventure stories were nothing but fabulous nonsense. Looking back we see the children's answer to this teaching in their rapid adoption of adult books such as *Robinson Crusoe* and *Gulliver's Travels*—an answer which indicates that children did not readily endorse the theories of their elders, zealous though the latter were in providing them with books that would improve their minds.

We have put aside this outmoded idea, yet we still need to devote much care to the selection of books for our children, even though our signposts are set in quite a different direction. Considering the mass of children's books that are available to-day, it would not be astonishing to find a sort of bewilderment on the part of parents confronted with the choice of books for their children. If, through literature, we are to influence conduct, then discrimination in the choice of books is as necessary to-day as in the days of hoop skirt and crinoline. Even though in recent years there has been a vast improvement in the production of children's books there are still many that are unsuitably illustrated, carelessly written, and badly produced. Discrimination in the choice of books is therefore necessary; books must be selected not only to entertain children, but, by skilful use of language, to enliven their imagination.

The Eighteenth Century and Earlier

Children's books of the eighteenth century and earlier do not figure prominently in this exhibition. There are, however, sufficient to indicate the state of literature for children before the opening of the nineteenth century. The exhibition gives special emphasis to the nineteenth century and the latter years of the eighteenth century as it was at this time that the first real attempts to write stories of real life for children began.

1 **Janeway, James.** A TOKEN FOR CHILDREN: being an exact account of the conversion, holy and exemplary lives and joyful deaths of several young children. *illustrated* 1671

2 **The Heavenly messenger,** *or,* THE CHILD'S PLAIN PATHWAY TO ETERNAL LIFE. Printed & sold by T. Evans, West Smithfield. *c*1700

3 **The Mad pranks and merry conceits of Tom Tram.** *second part.* Bow Church-yard, London. *c*1700

4 **The Reprobate's reward,** *or,* A LOOKING GLASS FOR DISOBEDIENT CHILDREN. Printed & sold by T. Evans, West Smithfield. *c*1700

5 **The History of Valentine and Orson.** Newly corrected and amended, with new pictures lively expressing the history. Dublin 1734

6 **Bunyan, John.** THE PILGRIM'S PROGRESS. 26*th* edition. *illustrated* 1743

7 **Bunyan, John.** DIVINE EMBLEMS, *or,* TEMPORAL THINGS SPIRITUALIZED FITTED FOR THE USE OF BOYS AND GIRLS. 10th edition. *illustrated* 1757

8 Another edition. *illustrated* 1802
Although children remember Bunyan by *Pilgrim's Progress,* which he did not write as a children's book, he was also the author of *A Book for boys and girls, or, Country Rhimes for Children* (1686). After Bunyan's death the title was changed to *Divine Emblems.* Under this title it went through numerous editions.

9 **The Renowned history of Valentine and Orson.** *illustrated* 1751

10 **Choice emblems, natural, historical, fabulous, moral and divine, for the improvement and pastime of youth.** *illustrated* 1772

11 **The youthful jester,** *or,* REPOSITORY OF WIT AND INNOCENT AMUSEMENT, containing moral and humourous tales, merry jests, laughable anecdotes, and smart repartees, the whole being as innocent as it is entertaining. Embellished with cuts. E. Newbery *c*1788

12 **Filial duty recommended and enforced.** *illustrated*
F. Newbery *c*1780

13 **The First principles of religion and the existence of a deity,** explained in a series of dialogues adapted to the capacity of the infant mind. *frontispiece* J. Marshall *c*1780

14 **'Soloman Sobersides.'** CHRISTMAS TALES FOR THE AMUSEMENT AND INSTRUCTION OF YOUNG LADIES AND GENTLEMEN. Printed by R. Marshall . . . who has ordered all the booksellers . . . to make a present of it to good girls and boys, they paying sixpence only to defray the expenses of binding. *illustrated*
R. Marshall *c*1780

15 **Berquin, A.** L'AMI DES ENFANS. No.\5 1782

16 **Berquin, A.** L'AMI DES ENFANS. Vol. II. London, Stockdale 1787

17 **A Course of lectures for Sunday evenings.** *frontispiece*
J. Marshall 1783

18 **Kilner, Dorothy.** LIFE AND PERAMBULATIONS OF A MOUSE. *illustrated* J. Marshall 1783

19 **School dialogues for boys ;** being an attempt to convey
20 instructions insensibly to their tender minds, and instil the love of virtue. 2 vols. J. Marshall 1783

21 **Moral and instructive tales for the improvement of young ladies,** calculated to amuse the mind and form the hearts to virtue. J. Marshall *c*1785

22 **Berquin, A.** THE CHILDREN'S FRIEND ; translated by Lucas
23 Williams. Vols. 1 & 2. *illustrated* Stockdale 1793

24 **Berquin, M.** THE HISTORY OF LITTLE GRANDISON. *frontispiece*
J. Stockdale 1791

25 **Princhard, Mrs.** THE BLIND CHILD. 2nd edition. *illustrated*
E. Newbery 1793

26 **Mental improvement for a young lady, on her entrance into the world ;** addressed to a favourite niece. *frontispiece*
W. Lane 1796

27 **The History of Guy, Earl of Warwick.** Printed for the company of walking stationers. *illustrated* Nottingham 1796

28 **Dramatic dialogues for the use of young persons** *illustrated*
E. Newbery 1792

29 **The Selector :** being a new and chaste collection of visions, tales, and allegories, calculated for the amusement and in-struction of the rising generation. *frontispiece*
E. Newbery 1797

6

30 **Youthful portraits ;** *or,* SKETCHES OF THE PASSIONS : exemplifying the dignity, and inculcating the advantages of virtue. *illustrated* E. Newbery 1796

31 **Day, Thomas.** THE HISTORY OF LITTLE JACK, embellished with twenty-six beautiful prints cut by Bewick.
J. Stockdale 1800

Moral Stories in Prose

The attempt to write stories of real life for children began late in the eighteenth century, and because of the very earnest tone of these stories the writers of them became known as the didactic school, which appellation later brought upon the heads of some worthy writers cynical comments which they did not wholly deserve.

32 **Always happy ! !** *or,* ANECDOTES OF FELIX AND HIS SISTER SERENA. *frontispiece* 1814

33 **Argus, Arabella.** OSTENTATION AND LIBERALITY : a tale. *illustrated* 1821

34 **Belson, Mary.** LITTLE LESSONS FOR LITTLE FOLKS. *frontispiece* 1818

35 **Berquin, A.** THE BLOSSOMS OF MORALITY. Illustrations designed and engraved by John Bewick. 3rd edition. 1801

This was the last book John Bewick illustrated, and appeared after his death.

36 **Berquin, A.** THE LOOKING-GLASS FOR THE MIND ; *or,* INTELLECTUAL MIRROR : being an elegant collection of the most delightful little stories and interesting tales. Illustrations designed and engraved by John Bewick. 1800

Arnaud Berquin was one of several French writers who influenced the development of childen's books in England. He is chiefly remembered by his collection of stories *L'Ami des enfans.*

37 **Cameron, Mrs. Lucy.** FORMS OF PRIDE. *frontispiece* 1829

38 **Cameron, Mrs. Lucy.** THE FRUITS OF EDUCATION. *frontispiece* 1827

39 **The Children in the wood :** a tale for the nursery. With copper plates. 1819

40 **Dame Partlet's farm ;** containing an account of the great riches she obtained by industry, the good life she led, and alas, good reader ! her sudden death. *illustrated* 1804

41 **Day, Thomas.** THE HISTORY OF SANDFORD AND MERTON. Vol. III. 9th ed.   1801
First appeared 1783-1789. A landmark in the history of children's books, It was issued in three parts. Only the last part has a frontispiece by Stothard which shows the reconciliation between Harry and Tommy, with the inevitable Barlow in the background.

42 **Early impressions,** *or,* MORAL AND INSTRUCTIVE ENTERTAINMENT FOR CHILDREN IN PROSE AND VERSE. Illustrations by Deighton in which the newly invented lithograph has displaced engravings as a medium of illustration.   1828

43 **Edgeworth, Maria.** MORAL TALES FOR YOUNG PEOPLE. Vol. 1.
                                                                    1802

44 **Elliott, Mary.** THE GIFT OF FRIENDSHIP, *or,* THE RIDDLE EXPLAINED. *illustrated*   1822

45 **Elliott, Mary.** PEGGY AND HER MAMMY. *illustrated*   1819

46 **Elliott, Mary.** THE TWO EDWARDS, *or,* PRIDE AND PREJUDICE UNMASKED. *illustrated*   1823

47 **Elliott, Mary.** THE WAX-TAPER, *or,* EFFECTS OF BAD HABITS. *illustrated*   1819

48 **The Godmother's tales.** *illustrated*   1808

49 **Goody Two Shoes** exemplifying the good consequences of early attention to learning and virtue. *illustrated*   1819

50 **The History of Primrose Prettyface** : who by her sweetness of temper, and love of learning, was raised from being the daughter of a poor cottager to great riches, and the dignity of lady of the manor. *illustrated*   New edition 1830
First published c1780.

51 **Hughes, Mary.** THE ALCHEMIST. *frontispiece*   1818

52 **Hughes, Mary.** THE ORNAMENTS DISCOVERED : a story in two parts. *illustrated*   1815

53 **Hughes, Mary.** STORIES FOR CHILDREN. *illustrated*   1819

54 **Kendal, E. A.** THE STORIES OF SENEX, *or,* LITTLE HISTORIES OF LITTLE PEOPLE. *frontispiece*   1800

55 **Mister, Mary.** THE ADVENTURES OF A DOLL ; compiled with the hope of affording amusement and instruction. *frontispiece*
                                                                    1816

56 **Mitchell, Miss M.** TALES OF INSTRUCTION AND AMUSEMENT. *frontispiece*   J. Harris 1807

57 **Pilkington, Mrs. M. H.** BIOGRAPHY FOR BOYS, *or,* Characteristic histories calculated to impress the youthful mind with an admiration of virtuous principles and a detestation of vicious ones. *frontispiece*   1800

8

58 **Pilkington, Mrs. M. H.** HENRY, *or*, THE FOUNDLING: to which are added, THE PREJUDICED PARENT, *or*, THE VIRTUOUS DAUGHTER. Tales calculated to improve the mind and morals of youth. *frontispiece.* 1799

59 **Pleasant tales to improve the mind and correct the morals of youth.** *frontispiece* 1801

60 **The Pretty portress of Windsor Lodge,** *or*, FILIAL AFFECTION REWARDED, in the instance of a royal protegee. A moral tale. *copper plates* *c*1830

61 **A Puzzle for a curious girl.** *illustrated* 1806

62 **Selwyn, A.** MONTAGUE PARK, *or*, FAMILY INCIDENTS. *illustrated* 1825

63 **Sherwood, Mrs.** THE HEDGE OF THORNS. *frontispiece* 1819

64 **Sherwood, Mrs.** THE HISTORY OF THEOPHILUS AND SOPHIA· 3rd edition. *frontispiece* 1819

65 **Sinclair, Catherine.** HOLIDAY HOUSE. Editions of 1839 and 1844.
   This book holds an important place in the development of the moral tale. In spite of the moral tone there is a real sense of fun and keen insight into the minds of children.

66 **Smith, Charlotte.** RAMBLES FARTHER: a continuation of
67   rural walks: in dialogues intended for the use of young persons. 2 vols. 2nd edition. 1800
   Dedicated to the Right Hon. Lady Georgiana Cavendish.

68 **Ventum, H.** TALES FOR DOMESTIC INSTRUCTION . . . *or*, THE NECESSITY OF CURBING OUR PASSIONS. *frontispiece* 1806

69 **The Winter scene ;** to amuse and instruct the rising generation. *illustrated* 1818

Moral Stories in Verse

While prose writers were teaching the rewards of virtue, writers of verse were no less earnest in the edification of the young. Their verses, full of admonition about neatness, honesty and generosity, had in many cases real merit, particularly those by Jane and Ann Taylor.

70 **Belson, Mary.** SIMPLE TRUTHS IN VERSE for the amusement and instruction of children at an early age. *frontispiece* 1816

71 **Elliott, Mary.** GEMS IN THE MINE, *or*, traits and habits of childhood in verse. *illustrated* 1824

72 **Goody Two Shoes,** *or*, THE HISTORY OF LITTLE MARGERY MEANWELL, in rhyme. *illustrated* 1825

73 **The Lily :** a book for children containing twenty-two trifles ; in verse adorned with cuts. 1817

74 The Poetical present for young ladies and gentlemen. *frontispiece* *c*1820

75 **Taylor, Ann and Jane.** ORIGINAL POEMS FOR INFANT MINDS. Vol. 1. 18th edition. *frontispiece* 1818

76 **Taylor, Ann and Jane.** SELECT RHYMES FOR THE NURSERY. *illustrated* 1809

77 *Also* : 10th ed. 1818

78 **Turner, Elizabeth.** THE DAISY, *or*, cautionary stories in verse. *illustrated with thirty engravings*
Facsimile copy of 1st edition published in 1807.

79 **Turner, Elizabeth.** THE COWSLIP, *or*, more cautionary stories in verse. 3rd edition. *illustrated* 1814

80 *Also* : Facsimile of the first edition. *illustrated* 1811

81 25th edition with engravings by S. Williams *c*1861

82 **Verses for little children.** With copper plates. 1816

83 **Watts, Isaac.** DIVINE SONGS ATTEMPTED IN EASY LANGUAGE FOR THE USE OF CHILDREN. *illustrated*

More Story than Moral

84 **Craik, Mrs. O. M.** HOW TO WIN LOVE, *or*, Rhoda's lesson. *illustrated* 1850

85 **Edgeworth, Maria.** HARRY AND LUCY. Parts 1 and 2 being
86 the first part of *Early lessons* by the author of *The Parents' Assistant.* 1801

87 **Ewing, Mrs. Juliana H.** DADDY DARWIN DAVICOT. Illustrated by Randolph Caldecott.

88 **Ewing, Mrs. Juliana H.** JACKANAPES. Illustrated by Randolph Caldecott.

89 **Ewing, Mrs. Juliana H.** LETS LIE-BY-THE-FIRE. Illustrated by Randolph Caldecott.

90 **Ewing, Mrs. Juliana H.** A FLAT IRON FOR A FARTHING. Illustrated by Mrs. Allingham.

91 **Ewing, Mrs. Juliana H.** JAN OF THE WINDMILL. Illustrated by Mrs. Allingham.

92 **Gatty, Mrs. A.** AUNT JUDY'S TALES. *illustrated* 1859

93 **Hall, Mrs. S. C.** THE HARTOPF JUBILEE, *or*, profit from play. *illustrated* 1840

94 **Howitt, Mary.** THE CHILDHOOD OF MARY LEESON. *frontispiece* 1848

95 **Marshall, Emma.** THE DAWN OF LIFE, *or*, Little Mildred's story. *illustrated* *c*1870

96 **Martineau, Harriet.** FIVE YEARS OF YOUTH, *or*, sense and sentiment. *illustrated* 1831

97 **(Molesworth, Mrs. M. L.) Graham, Ennis.** "CARROTS": just a little boy. Illustrated by Walter Crane. 1876

98 **Yonge, Charlotte M.** THE LANCES OF LYNWOOD. *illustrated* 1855

Books of Fun and Nonsense

The spirit of comical nonsense, always difficult to suppress in the English character, bobbed up its merry head at frequent intervals throughout this good-behaviour period.

99 **Anecdotes and adventures of fifteen gentlemen.** *coloured illustrations* J. Marshall *c*1820

100 **The Comical capering Willy goat.** *coloured illustrations* G. Martin *c*1810

101 **Courtship and marriage of Jerry and Kitty.** *coloured illustrations* J. Harris 1814

102 **Dame Dodge and her dog Tray,** in verse. *coloured illustrations* J. Bysh *c*1825

103 **Dame Trot and her comical cats.** *coloured illustrations* Dean *c*1830

104 **The Death and burial of Cock Robin.** *coloured illustrations* G. Martin *c*1810

105 **The Doleful death of poor old Robin,** with the distribution of his valuable property as related and exhibited in beautiful engravings by Peter Prins. *coloured illustrations* J. Harris 1814

106 **Gaffer Grandy and his dog Rover.** *coloured illustrations* G. Martin *c*1810

107 **The History of Johnny Gilpin.** Price sixpence. *coloured illustrations* G. Martin *c*1810

108 **The History of sixteen wonderful old women.** *coloured illustrations* J. Harris 1820

109 *also*: same edition arranged as a panorama.

110 **The House that Jack built.** *coloured illustrations* J. Marshall 1821

111 **Jack and Jill.** *coloured illustrations* G. Martin *c*1810

112　**The Life and death of Cock Robin,** adorned with coloured plates. *coloured illustrations* J. Bysh *c*1830

113　**A Manuscript version of The Old woman and her pig.** Written and illustrated in colour by Eleanor Mure between 1828 and 1832.

114　**A Manuscript version of The Three Bears.** Written and illustrated in colour by Eleanor Mure 1831. With an original ending showing the three bears throwing the old woman to the top of St. Paul's Cathedral.

115　**Memoirs of the little man and the little maid.** *coloured illustrations* Tabart 1807

116　**The Monkey's frolic,** a humorous tale in verse. *coloured illustrations* *c*1840

117　**Old Mother Hubbard and her dog.** *coloured illustrations* *c*1840

118　**The Old woman and her pig.** *coloured illustrations* G. Martin *c*1810

119　**The Peacock "At Home".** *line illustrations* 1807

120　*also :* 1808 edition with coloured illustrations.

121　**Peter Piper's practical principles of plain and perfect pronunciation.** *coloured illustrations* J. Harris 1820

122　**The Royal Eagle's feast and ball, by Jenny Wren who saw it all.** *coloured illustrations* *c*1815

123　**Trial of Cock Sparrow.** *coloured illustrations* *c*1810

124　**Whittington and his cat.** *coloured illustrations* J. Harris *c*1820

125　**Young Nibble the discontented mouse.** *coloured illustrations* Dean *c*1830

126　**A Book of nonsense by Edward Lear.** *coloured illustrations*

Cut-out Figures & Moveable Books

The recent revival in the production of Cut-out books and Moveable books adds interest to the Moveable books of the 19th century. Moveable toys sufficiently compact to be issued within covers were not devised until about 1840. Before this date invention was confined to Cut-out figures issued by S. & J. Fuller which enjoyed a wide circulation for at least twenty years.

127　**Frank Feignwell's attempts to amuse his friends.** S. & J. Fuller 1811

128　**History of Little Fanny.** S. & J. Fuller 1810

129 Lucinda, the orphan.   S. & J. Fuller 1812
130 Young Albert the Roscius.   S. & J. Fuller 1811
131 Rose Merton the little orphan.   Dean & Son c1850
     The incidents described in crude rhymes are similar to
     those in The History of Little Fanny, published earlier in the
     century.
132 Cock Robin.   Dean & Son c1850
133 Old Mother Hubbard.   Dean & Son c1850
134 The Boy's own royal acting Punch and Judy.
                                           Dean & Son c1860
135 The Realm of the queen of flowers.   c1860
136 The Wonder book of nature's transformations.
                                           Ward Lock c1860
137 Little Folks' Peepshow.   Ernest Nister c1890

The Animal Story

Stories about animals, both realistic and fanciful, now so prominent
a feature in many publishers' lists, had their beginnings in 1786 when
Mrs. Trimmer wrote *Fabulous Histories, or, the history of the robins,
designed for the instruction of children respecting their treatment of animals.*
The Trimmers of that age were acutely conscious of the superiority of
man to the brute creation, consequently the animals depicted in the
stories are merely dummies talking moral platitudes.

138 **Argus, Arabella.** THE ADVENTURES OF A DONKEY. *frontispiece*
                                                             1823
139 **Biography of a spaniel.** *frontispiece*   1826
140 **Bob, the spotted terrier,** *or*, MEMOIRS OF THE DOG OF KNOW-
     LEDGE, supposed to be written by himself. *illustrated* 1821
141 **The Dog of Knowledge,** *or*, MEMOIRS OF BOB, THE SPOTTED
     TERRIER. *frontispiece*   1801
142 **Elliott, Mary.** CONFIDENTIAL MEMOIRS, *or*, adventures of a
     parrot, a greyhound, a cat, and a monkey. *illustrated* 1821
143 **The History of Frugal the wild bee,** by Mr. Frankly. *coloured
     frontispiece*   1816
144 **The History of a goldfinch.** *coloured woodcut*   1807
145 **(Kendal, E. A.)** THE CANARY BIRD: a moral fiction, inter-
     spersed with poetry. *frontispiece*   E. Newbery 1799
146 **Kendal, E. A.** THE CRESTED WREN. *illustrated*
                                               E. Newbery 1799

147 **Kendal, E. A.** KEEPER'S TRAVELS IN SEARCH OF HIS MASTER. *frontispiece* E. Newbery 1798

148 Another copy 5th edition 1809 from Florence Nightingale's nursery library.

149 **Kilner, Dorothy.** THE LIFE AND PERAMBULATIONS OF A MOUSE. 2 vols. *illustrated* 1819
For earlier edition see No. 18.

150 **Little Downy,** *or,* THE HISTORY OF A FIELD-MOUSE : a moral tale embellished with twelve coloured engravings. 1822

151 **Mary and her cat in words not exceeding two syllables.** *illustrated* 1821

152 **Mungo, the little traveller,** a work compiled for the instruction and amusement of youth. 2nd edition. *frontispiece* 1814

153 **Sandham, Miss.** THE BEE AND THE BUTTERFLY, *or,* industry and idleness. *illustrated* 1824

154 **Sherwood, Mrs.** THE LITTLE WOODMAN AND HIS DOG CAESAR. 12th edition. *illustrated* 1828

155 **Trimmer, Mrs. Sarah.** FABULOUS HISTORIES, *or,* the history of the robins designed for the instruction of children respecting their treatment of animals. 12th edition. *woodcuts by John Bewick* 1818

156 Later edition 1844. *illustrated*

157 **(Tucker, Charlotte M.)** THE RAMBLES OF A RAT. *frontispiece* 1861

Beatrix Potter

158 **Potter, Beatrix.** THE TALE OF PETER RABBIT. The privately printed edition, undated.
The author had this book printed at her own expense. There were five hundred copies and she sold them to her friends at one-and-twopence each.

159 **Potter, Beatrix.** THE TAILOR OF GLOUCESTER. The privately printed edition December 1902.
Encouraged by the success of Peter Rabbit, the author had four hundred copies printed at the cost of £40. Warne the publisher accepted the book but it was rewritten, shortened and new pictures were added.
Both privately printed editions are now collector's treasures.

160 **Potter, Beatrix.** THE ROLY-POLY PUDDING.
Shows the format as first issued in 1908. When it assumed the well-known dumpy format its title was changed to *The Tale of Mr. Sammy Whiskers.*
Other first editions include :

161 THE TALE OF MRS. TIGGY-WINKLE.   1905
162 THE PIE AND THE PATTY-PAN.   1905
163 THE TALE OF THE FLOPSY BUNNIES.   1909
164 THE TALE OF MRS. TITTLEMOUSE.   1910
165 THE TALE OF TIMMY TIPTOES.   1911
166 THE TALE OF PIGLING BLAND.   1913

Fables

The earliest form of literature which attracted children was the moral lesson-book of the talking-beast kind, in which animals assume human characteristics, speech and action.   It was not, however, the moral in the allegory that attracted so many children to Aesop and Reynard.   The interest of children is captured by the resourceful and adventurous hero, or by the triumphs and intrigues of the crafty animal against beasts larger than himself.   David in *Jack the giant-killer* has them firmly on his side in the conflict with the giant.

167 **Aesop.** FABELLAE ALIQUOT AESOPICAE IN USUM PUERORUM SELECTAE. *illustrated*   Plantin 1566

168 **Aesop.** FABULAE AESOPI . . . IN USUM SCHOLARUM.
Amsterdam 1672

169 **Aesop.** THE FABLES OF AESOP AND OTHERS with instructive applications, adapted to all capacities . . . by S. Croxall. *illustrated*   1802

170 **Dodsley, R.** SELECT FABLES OF ESOP AND OTHER FABULISTS. *illustrated*   1802

171 **Gay, John.** FABLES.   Woodcuts by Thomas & John Bewick.
1796

172 **Gay, John.** FABLES.   With 67 coloured engravings.   1821

173 **Godwin, William.** FABLES ANCIENT AND MODERN, adapted for
174 the use of children from three to eight years of age.   Adorned with thirty-six copper plates.
2 vols.   1st edition 1805

175 *also*: 2nd edition 1806.   The illustrations are almost certainly
176 by Mulready, but are sometimes ascribed to Blake.

177 **The Mother's fables in verse.**   Designed through the medium of amusement, to convey to the minds of children some useful precepts of virtue and benevolence.   *illustrated* Darton 1818

178 **Old Friends in a new dress,** *or*, FAMILIAR FABLES IN VERSE.
Darton 1820

15

Fairy Tales

The persistence of fairy tales is a significant feature in the development of children's literature. In Puritan times when children were persuaded to be busy with their catechisms, or Clarke's *General Martyrologie* by way of lighter reading, fairy tales were then frowned upon ; they were evil and pernicious.

179 **Aladin,** *or,* THE WONDERFUL LAMP. *illustrated* Tabart 1808

180 **Aladdin,** *or,* THE WONDERFUL LAMP. *illustrated*
Edinburgh 1809
In vol. III of the New Juvenile Library.

181 **Ali Baba,** *or,* THE FORTY THIEVES. *illustrated* Tabart 1807

182 **Andersen, Hans C.** WONDERFUL STORIES FOR CHILDREN. Translated from the Danish by Mary Howitt. *illustrated*
1846

One of the earliest translations into English of Andersen's fairy stories for children.

183 **Craik, Mrs. O. M.** THE FAIRY BOOK. 1863

184 **Craik, Mrs. O. M.** THE LITTLE LAME PRINCE. *illustration by J. McL. Ralston* 1875

185 **Cruikshank, George.** FAIRY LIBRARY. Hop-o'-My-Thumb ; Jack and the Bean-stalk ; Cinderella ; Puss in Boots. *illustrated* 1874

186 **De Morgan, Mary.** THE NECKLACE OF PRINCESS FLORIMONDE. *illustrated by Walter Crane* 1880

187 **De Morgan, Mary.** ON A PINCUSHION. *illustration by William De Morgan.* 2nd edition. 1877

188 **Ewing, Juliana H.** OLD-FASHIONED FAIRY TALES. *c*1877

189 **Fairy tales from the Arabian nights.** *illustrated by J. O. Batten* 1893

190 **Frere, Mary.** OLD DECCAN DAYS. 1881

191 **Graham, Ennis (Mrs. Molesworth).** TELL ME A STORY. *illustrated by Walter Crane* 1875

192 **Grimm, M. M.** GRIMM'S GOBLINS. German popular stories, with 24 illustrations after George Cruikshank. 1877

193 **Grimm, M. M.** HOUSEHOLD STORIES. *illustrated by Walter Crane* 1882

194 **The History of Fortunio.** *illustrated* Edinburgh 1809
In vol. V of the New Juvenile Library.

16

THE

H E D G E

OF

Thorns.

BY MRS. SHERWOOD,

Author of " The History of the Fairchild Family,"
" Little Henry and his Bearer," &c.

LONDON.

PRINTED FOR J. HATCHARD,

190, PICCADILLY.

1819.

A. Mills Delin.

J. Mills Sculp.

The Hedge of Thorns.

little Bull attempting to get through the Hedge.

page 5

195　**History of Jack the giant-killer.** *illustrated*

Edinburgh 1809

In vol. IV of the New Juvenile Library.

196　**The History of the white cat.** *illustrated*　　　Tabart 1808

197　**Housman, Laurence.** A FARM IN FAIRYLAND. *illustrated by the author*　1894

198　**Jacobs, Joseph.** ENGLISH FAIRY TALES. *illustrated by John D. Batten*　1890

199　**Kingsley, Charles.** THE WATER-BABIES : a fairy tale for a land-baby. *illustrated by J. Noel-Paton*　1863

200　**Lemon, Mark.** THE ENCHANTED DOLL : a fairy tale for little people. *illustrated by Richard Doyle.*　1849

201　**Lemon, Mark.** FAIRY TALES. *illustrated by Richard Doyle and Charles H. Bennett*　1868

202　**Macdonald, George.** AT THE BACK OF THE NORTH WIND. *illustrated by Arthur Hughes*　1871

203　**Macdonald, George.** DEALINGS WITH THE FAIRIES. *illustrated by Arthur Hughes*　1868

204　**Mackarness, Mrs.** THE DREAM CHINTZ. *illustrated by James Godwin*　1851

205　**Nurse Dandlem's little repository of great instruction** containing the surprising adventures of Little Wake Wilful, and his deliverance from the giant Grumbolumbo . . . for the sole amusement of the Chickabiddy generation. *illustrated*

Glasgow J. Lumsden c1810

206　**Parry, Edward Abbott.** BUTTERSCOTED, *or,* a cheap trip to fairy land. *illustrated by Archie Macgregor.*　1896

207　**Ruskin, John.** THE KING OF THE GOLDEN RIVER. *illustrated by Richard Doyle.* 2nd edition.　1851

208　**Ruskin, John.** THE KING OF THE GOLDEN RIVER. *illustrated by Arthur Rackham*　1932

209　**Sharp, Evelyn.** ALL THE WAY TO FAIRY LAND. *illustrated by Mrs. Percy Dearmer*　1898

210　**Steel, Flora Annie.** TALES OF THE PUNJAB. *illustrated by J. Lockwood Kipling*　1894

211　**The Story of the white cat.** *illustrated*　　　Edinburgh 1809

In vol. VI of the New Juvenile Library.

212　**Tales from the Court of Oberon** *with sixteen illustrations by Alfred Crowquill*　c1850

Robinson Crusoe & Robinsonnades

Adventure stories are a main feature in a children's library to-day, all of them no doubt owing filial duty to Daniel Defoe, whose *Robinson Crusoe* appeared in 1719, and some to the first English translation of the Swiss story, *The Swiss Family Robinson*, which appeared in 1814. The gap between *Robinson Crusoe*, a book written for adults, and so readily appropriated by children, and the adventure story as we know it to-day, is so wide that it becomes one of the major mysteries in the development of children's literature. The milk-and-water Crusoe stories, commonly known as Robinsonnades, written during the 1820's or thereabouts, have long since been treated to the fate they well deserve.

213   **Defoe, Daniel.** THE LIFE AND STRANGE SURPRISING ADVENTURES OF ROBINSON CRUSOE. *illustrated.*
      vol. I   8th edition   1736

214   vol. II   6th edition.   1736

215   *Also*: 15th edition.   1778

216   *Also*: John Mayer's edition 1831. *illustrated by George Cruik-*
217   *shank.* 2 vols.

218   *Also*: Tabart edition 1805, revised for the use of young persons.

219   *Also*: An abridged edition pubilshed by H. Kent. *illustrated*

220   **Robinson Crusoe Penny Chapbook.**   Rusher Banbury

221- **Campe, J. H.** THE NEW ROBINSON CRUSOE : an instructive
224   and entertaining history for the use of children of both sexes. Translated from the French. *illustrated by John Bewick.* 4 vols.   1788

       Rousseau was the source of inspiration of this book about a castaway who met his adventures not in the course of nature, but through defective education.

225   Another edition in one volume 1789

226   **The English hermit,** *or*, THE ADVENTURES OF PHILIP QUARLL. *illustrated*   *c*1790

       The taste for desert island stories by Defoe was continued in a few so-called Robinsonnades, of which one of the most popular was the *Adventures of Philip Quarll*, the English hermit. Although this story was originally published in 1727 it lasted in various abridged and chap book versions until well on in the nineteenth century.

227   Another version. 1809

228 Another version. 1816

229 Another version. 1830

230 **Elliott, Mary.** THE ENGLISH HERMIT, *or*, the adventures of Philip Quarle. *illustrated* 1822

231 **Hofland, Mrs. B.** THE YOUNG CRUSOE, *or*, the shipwrecked boy. *frontispiece* *c*1825

232 **Strickland, Agnes.** THE RIVAL CRUSOES, *or*, the shipwreck. *illustrated* (1826)

Adventure

From 1719 to 1856 is a considerable period in literary history, and yet it was not until the publication of *The young fur traders* by R. M. Ballantyne in the fifties of last century, that writers of adventure stories hit upon the idea that boys and girls were different from the 'children' and 'babies' for whom most children's authors had written up to that date. Ballantyne was the first of the modern writers who fully understood that boys wanted a tale, not a story book, nor a boyish book, but a downright tale of adventure.

233 **Ballantyne, R. M.** THE CORAL ISLAND. *illustrated by the author* 1858

234 **Ballantyne, R. M.** SNOWFLAKES AND SUNBEAMS, *or*, THE YOUNG FUR TRADERS. *illustrated by the author* 1856

235 **Collingwood, Harry.** THE PIRATE ISLAND. *illustrated* 1885

236 **Fenn, G. Manville.** REAL GOLD. *illustrated* 1894

237 **Haggard, H. Rider.** KING SOLOMON'S MINES. 1885

238 **Henty, G. A.** UNDER DRAKE'S FLAG. *illustrated* 1883

239 **Kingston, W. H. G.** THE SOUTH SEA WHALER. *illustrated* 1875

245 **Kingston, W. H. G.** THE THREE LIEUTENANTS. *illustrated* 1875

241 **Kipling, Rudyard.** CAPTAINS COURAGEOUS. *illustrated* 1897

242-
244 **Marryat, Captain.** MASTERMAN READY. 3 vols. *illustrated* 1845

245 **O'Grady, Standish.** THE CHAIN OF GOLD. *illustrated* 1895

246 **Reid, Mayne.** RAN AWAY TO SEA. *illustrated* 1859

247 **Stables, Gordon.** THE CRUISE OF THE SNOWBIRD. *illustrated* 1890

248 **Stevenson, R. L.** TREASURE ISLAND. *illustrated edition* 1886

The School Story

Arranged chronologically.

The old style of school story has few devotees to-day. There is, however, still room for the children's school story provided writers who attempt such books are wide awake to modern trends in education and social development.

249 **Pelham, M.** FIRST GOING TO SCHOOL, *or*, the story of Tom Brown and his sisters. *illustrated* 1809

250 **Lamb, Charles and Mary.** MRS. LEICESTER'S SCHOOL, *or*, the history of several young ladies related by themselves. 4th edition. *frontispiece* 1814

251 **Adams, William.** THE CHERRY-STONES, *or*, the face of conscience : a tale of Charlton School. 5th edition. 1857

252 **Farrar, Frederic W.** ERIC : *or*, little by little. *illustrated by Gordon Browne* 1894
First published 1858.

253 **Hughes, Thomas.** TOM BROWN'S SCHOOL DAYS. 7th edition. 1860

254 **Adams, H. C.** WHO DID IT ? *or*, Holmwood Priory. *illustrated* 1882

255 **Reed, Talbot Baines.** THE COCK-HOUSE AT FELLOGARTH. *illustrated* 1891

256 **Meade, L. T.** BETTY, A SCHOOL GIRL. *illustrated* 1895

257 **Avery, Harold.** FRANK'S FIRST TERM. 1896

258 **Home, Andrew.** FROM FAG TO MONITOR. *illustrated* 1896

259 **Kipling, Rudyard.** STALKY AND CO. 1899

Sedate Periodicals

Arranged chronologically.

The enterprise recently shown by Messrs. Collins in publishing a monthly children's magazine adds interest to this section of the exhibition. The short-lived success of the earliest magazines is easily understood. The editor in her address to young readers in *The Juvenile Magazine* published by J. Marshall in January 1788 clearly states that her pages are addressed to "my young friends, who are fond of instruction"—a statement quite sufficient to put the youngsters on their guard.

260 **The Juvenile magazine,** *or*, an instructive and entertaining miscellany for youth of both sexes. *illustrated*
John Marshall 1788
One of the earliest attempts at a periodical for children. It ran only for one year.

21

261 **The Young misses magazine.** vol. 1.   Edinburgh 1795

262 **The Monthly Preceptor,** *or,* JUVENILE LIBRARY. vol. 1.   1800
   The object of this monthly periodical is mainly concerned
   with the education of youth. Scholars were provided with
   questions each month, for which prizes were awarded. Both
   'young gentlemen' and 'young ladies' were competitors.
   Amongst the young competitors who became famous later in
   life were : John Baxter, Josiah Conder, W. J. Fox, H. Leigh
   Hunt, Thomas Love Peacock, and Thomas De Quincey.
   Leigh Hunt appears to have been a most persistent com-
   petitor. One month he received a silver medal for an essay
   "On humanity in the brute creation". In another number
   we are informed that Master H. L. Hunt, "whose information
   is extensive, and his genius luxuriant . . . only requires a little
   attention to arrangement, and to study the art of arts, the art
   to blot".

263 **The Select magazine for the instruction and amusement
   of young persons.** vol. 1.   1822

264 **The Children's Friend** for the year 1824. Edited by the Rev.
   W. Carus Wilson. vol. 1. *illustrated*   Kirkby Lonsdale
   The Child's companion and *The Children's friend* were the
   earliest serial publications for the young which secured long
   and continuous life as genuine periodicals.

265 **The Children's Friend** for 1882.

266 **The Child's Companion,** *or,* Sunday scholars reward. vol. 1.
   illustrated   1824

267 **The Child's Companion,** *or,* Sunday scholars reward. 12
   monthly parts for 1834.

268 **The Child's Companion** for 1858.

269- **The National School magazine.** vols. 1 and 2. 1824 & 1825
270

271 **The Nursery and infants school magazine.** Edited by Mrs.
   Cameron. *illustrated*   1831

272 **The Baptist children's magazine and sabbath scholars'
   reward.** vol. III. *illustrated*   1834

273 **The Teacher's offering,** *or,* SUNDAY-SCHOOL MONTHLY VISITOR
   for 1838. *illustrated*

274 **The Boy's own magazine.** vol. 4. *illustrated*   1858

275 **The Children's prize.** Edited by J. Erskine Clarke. *illustrated*
   First published in 1864.   1871

276 **The Picture magazine in easy words.** No. 131.

November 1864

277 **Aunt Judy's magazine.** Edited by Mrs. Alfred Gatty. 1866

The first volume of a famous periodical. Page 123 contains a review of *Alice in wonderland.*

278 **Little Wide-awake.** No. 4. *illustrated* April 1868

279 *also :* complete volume for 1880.

280 **Good words for the young.** Edited by George Macdonald. vol. 1. *illustrated* 1869

281 **The Child's Pictorial,** a monthly coloured magazine. vol. 1.

May to December 1885

Mrs. J. H. Ewing and Mrs. Molesworth were closely associated with this periodical, which had a very short life.

282 **Boy's Own Paper.** No. 412. December 1886

Sensational Periodicals

If the magazines shown in the previous section were giants of respectability in the nineteenth century world of children's periodicals, a similar status would hardly be claimed for the blood-and-thunder magazines which began to appear round about 1870. The first of these periodicals, *The Boys of England, a young gentlemen's journal of sport, travel, fun and instruction,* subscribed to by His Royal Highness Prince Arthur, began in 1866. It had sixteen large pages, well printed and illustrated, all for one penny, and could easily be folded and carried in the schoolboy's pocket. In six months the editor claimed a circulation of 150,000 copies. The production of this type of magazine, considered by many slip-shod and illiterate in style, must now run into hundreds of thousands weekly.

283 **The Boys of England,** a young gentleman's journal of sport, sensation, fun and instruction conducted by E. J. Brett. vol. III. 1867

The first sensational penny magazine for boys.

284- **Boys of the Empire.** Edited by Edwin J. Brett. Nos. 266
287   to 269.

288 **Jack Harkaway adventures.** Edited by Edwin J. Brett.

289- **The Blue dwarf.** A tale of love, mystery and crime. Percy
291   B. St. John. 3 vols.

Coloured Books 1800-1840

The first quarter of the nineteenth century proclaims itself as a new era in the illustration of books for children. Many books between 1800 and 1840 were enlivened by gaily-coloured illustrations, some of them of high decorative quality. Seldom is the name of the artist disclosed, although often the pictures were drawn by artists of repute. Many of the books were published by John Harris, who ranked first among his contemporaries in this field. Clear engraving, spirited woodcuts and later the newly-discovered lithograph process, were all used to make attractive to children nursery rhymes, nonsense alphabets, multiplication tables, and other instructive and recreational books.

292 **Little George.** 1801

293 **The adventures of Jack the broom boy.** 1807

294 **Little Warbler of the cottage and her dog Constant.** 1816

295 **Vicissitude,** *or,* the life and adventures of Ned Frolic. 1818

296 **Rambles of a butterfly.** By Mary Belson. 1819

297 **Baby tales.** *c*1820

298 **Cock Robin and Jenny Wren.** *c*1820

299 **Gaping, wide-mouthed waddling frog.** A new and entertaining game of questions and commands, embellished with sixteen coloured engravings. *c*1820

300 **Infants' own book.** *c*1820

301 **Wonders of nature and art.** *c*1820

302 **Blue Beard,** *or,* THE EFFECTS OF FEMALE CURIOSITY. In easy verse. By Miss Horwood. 1821

303 **Christmas tales,** by Solomon Sobersides. 1821

304 **Coloured panoramic view of the French Army.** 1829

305 **The History of Little Henry and his bearer.** By Mrs. Sherwood. 25th edition. 1829

306 **The Whole art of Legerdemain,** *or,* THE CONJUROR UNMASKED. *c*1830

307 **Tragical history of the children in the wood.** *c*1840

Coloured Books 1840-1870

This period shows the great change which the art of lithography was destined to effect. An examination of these illustrations is not likely to inspire anyone with enthusiasm for the state of English pictorial art at this period.

308 **Aunt Friendly's nursery Keepsake.** Printed in colours by Kronheim.

309 **Child's play.** (Nursery rhymes) *illustrated by Hon. Mrs. E. V. Boyle.*

310 **Grandmamma Wise,** *or,* A VISIT TO ROSE COTTAGE. *illustrated*

311 **How Patty learned the alphabet.**

312 **Little Frank at the farm.**

313 **Old Ginger Bread and the schoolboys.**

314- **The Parents cabinet.** 2 vols.
315

316 **Perseverance.** A tale. By Charles Cowden Clark. *illustrated by John Absolon.* 1844

317 **Peter Parley's Annual.** 1857

318 **Playing at Settlers.** By Mrs. Lee. *illustrated by John Gilbert.* 1855

319 **Strafford, Miss E.** TALES OF DELIGHT FOR YOUTHFUL READERS. *illustrated*

320 **Tommy Trot.**

321 **A Visit to Aunt Agnes.**

Notable Illustrators in Line and Colour

WALTER CRANE, KATE GREENAWAY, RANDOLPH CALDECOTT

From about 1870 onwards, better picture books for the nursery displaced the crude, inartistic productions of the fifties. The giants of this period were Walter Crane, Kate Greenaway and Randolph Caldecott, whose work was presented to the gaze of children through the medium of the skilful colour-printer Edmund Evans.

WALTER CRANE

Walter Crane's work was decorative ; his illustrations were drawn to harmonise with types and printers' ornaments, and to form with them a comprehensive and unified design.

322 **The Baby's bouquet.** A fresh bunch of old rhymes and tunes arranged and decorated by Walter Crane. Routledge

323 **The Baby's opera.** A book of old rhymes with new dresses, by Walter Crane. Routledge

324 **The Baby's own Aesop.** Being the fables condensed in rhyme with portable morals, pictorially painted by Walter Crane. Routledge

325- **Walter Crane's Toy Books.** Sixpenny series, published by
329   G. Routledge.
    1. Jack and the Beanstalk.
    2. Little Red Riding Hood.
    3. The Sleeping Beauty.
    4. Cinderella.
    5. Baby's own alphabet.

330- **Walter Crane's Toy Books.** Shilling series published by
331   G. Routledge.
    1. Beauty and the Beast.
    2. Goody Two Shoes.

332- **Walter Crane's Bound Picture Books,** published by G.
334   Routledge.
    1. The song of soxpence picture book.   1865
    2. The Bluebeard picture book.   1873
    3. The Three bears picture book.   1876

KATE GREENAWAY

The work of Kate Greenaway was romantic rather than decorative. The sincerity of the drawings, their modesty, humour and love and understanding of children, reflect the tenderness and grace of mind of the artist herself.

335 **Almanack for 1884.** By Kate Greenaway.

336 **Book of Games.** By Kate Greenaway.   Routledge.

337 **A Day in a child's life.** *illustrated by Kate Greenaway*.
    Routledge

338 **Frontispiece and title pages to The Girl's Own Annual for 1886.** *illustrated by Kate Greenaway*.

339 **Little Ann and other poems.** By Jane and Ann Taylor.
    illustrated by Kate Greenaway   Routledge

340 **Marigold garden.** Pictures and rhymes by Kate Greenaway. Printed in colours by Edmund Evans.   Routledge

341 **Mother Goose,** *or,* The Old nursery rhymes. Illustrated by Kate Greenaway. Engraved and printed by Edmund Evans.
    Routledge

342 **Turnaside Cottage.** By Mary S. Clark. *illustrated by Kate Greenaway*   1875
    One of the artist's earliest efforts at book illustration.

343 **Under the window.** Pictures and rhymes for children. By Kate Greenaway.   Routledge

Caldecott's work was realistic and graphic rather than decorative or romantic. The pictures, lively and robust as they are, help to interpret the text of the book illustrated ; this makes the artist's series of nursery books still a source of enjoyment to both children and adults.

344 **Complete set of Randolph Caldecott's picture books** of first issued by Geogreg Routledge & Sons.

345 **Eight coloured illustrations** from the Routledge edition of *The Three jovial huntsmen.*

Other Notable Illustrators in Line & Colour

Some of these books show what the illustrators thought about art and illustration, with little regard to what children might like in the way of a picture. A fault just as common to-day as in the nineteenth century.

346 **Batten, John D.** THE BOOK OF WONDER VOYAGES. 1896

347 **Bedford, Francis D.** A BOOK OF NURSERY RHYMES. *c*1890

348- **Blake, William.** TALES FROM SHAKESPEARE. By Charles
349 Lamb. *illustrated by William Blake.* 2 vols. 1810

350 **Boyle, Mrs. E. V.** THE STORY WITHOUT AN END. 1879

351 **Browne, F. Gordon.** NONSENSE FOR SOMEBODY. 1896

352 **Cruikshank, George.** THE HORKEY : a ballad by Robert Bloomfield. *illustrated by George Cruikshank* 1882

353 **Cruikshank, George.** THE MAN IN THE MOON. By Horace Lennard. *illustrated by George Cruikshank* 1884

354 **Doyle, Richard.** THE PRINCESS NOBODY. By Andrew Lang, after the drawings by Richard Doyle. Printed in colours by Edmund Evans.

354a **Dulac, Edmund.** STORIES FROM THE ARABIAN NIGHTS. Retold by Laurence Housman. With drawing by Edmund Dulac 1907

354b **Ford, Henry J.** THE BOOK OF ROMANCE. Edited by Andrew Lang. *illustrated by H. J. Ford.* 1902

355 **Griset, Ernest.** THE HATCHET THROWERS. By James Greenwood, with thirty-six illustrations, drawn in wood, by Ernest Griset. 1866

Griset was one of the most individual illustrators of the sixties.

356 **Housman, Laurence.** GOBLIN MARKET. By Christina Rossetti. *illustrated by Laurence Housman* 1893

357 **Hughes, Arthur.** SING-SONG : a nursery-rhyme book by Christina Rossetti. *illustrated by Arthur Hughes* 1872

358 **Hughes, Arthur.** SPEAKING LIKENESSES. By Christina Rossetti, with pictures thereof by Arthur Hughes. 1874

359 **Marks, H. Stacey.** THE GOOD OLD DAYS, *or,* Christmas under Queen Elizabeth. By Esmé Stuart. *with illustrations in colour by H. Stacey Marks* 1876

360 **Rackham, Arthur.** MOTHER GOOSE : the old nursery rhymes. *illustrated by Arthur Rackham.*

361 **Robinson, Charles.** A CHILD'S GARDEN OF VERSES. By Robert Louis Stevenson. *illustrated by Charles Robinson* 1896

362 **Robinson, Charles.** LILLIPUT LYRICS. By W. B. Rands. Edited by R. Brimley Johnson. *illustrated by Charles Robinson* 1899

363 **Shaw, Byam.** OLD KING COLE'S BOOK OF NURSERY RHYMES. Illustrated by Byam Shaw. Engraved and printed by Edmund Evans.

364 **Sullivan, E. J.** TOM BROWN'S SCHOOL DAYS. *with illustrations by Edmund J. Sullivan* 1896

365 **Tenniel, John.** ALICE'S ADVENTURES IN WONDERLAND. By Lewis Carroll. *with forty-two illustrations by John Tenniel.* 1868

366 **Thomson, Hugh.** JACK THE GIANT-KILLER. One of Hugh Thomson's illustrated fairy books. 1898

367 **Upton, Florence K.** ADVENTURES OF TWO DUTCH DOLLS. 1896

367a **Upton, Florence K.** THE GOLLIWOG'S FOX-HUNT.

Books of Instruction

The books exhibited in this section are mainly confined to a selection of those published between 1700 and 1830.

ALPHABETS

368 **A History of the apple pie written by Z.** J. Harris 1808

> The apple pie's life, as the subject for an ABC, extends at least from the 17th century to Kate Greenaway.

368a *also* : another edition published by C. Bysh *c*1830

369 **A Selection of Battledores.** *c*1810 - 1830
The earliest form of ABC, the hornbook, subsequently came to be made in the shape of a battledore, when the letters were often engraved direct on to wood or metal, instead of being printed on a square of paper and covered with a piece of horn. The name survived in these cardboard folders.

370 **The Silver penney for the amusement and instruction of good children.** Kendrew, York *c*1820

371 **The Infants' alphabet.** Dean & Munday 1823

372 **Cock Robin alphabet.** Park *c*1840

373 **The Alphabet of peace.** Darton *c*1857

374 **Mama's little pet's A.B.C.** Read & Co. *c*1870

375 **The Railway alphabet.** Dean & Son *c*1880

READING, WRITING & ARITHMETIC

376 **Coffin, W.** A HELP TO TRUE SPELLING AND READING, *or*, a very easie method for the teaching children, or elder persons, rightly to spell, and exactly to read English. 1705

377 **Collyer, J.** READING MADE EASY. *illustrated*
Nottingham 1781

378 **Three specimens of Spelling Sheets** published about 1800.

379 **Smith, T.** AN EASY SPELLING BOOK. *illustrated* Derby *c*1800

380 **Fenning, Daniel.** THE UNIVERSAL SPELLING BOOK. *illustrated*
1804

381 Another edition 1827

382 **Cottage Lessons.** *illustrated* 1817

383 **Howe's Primer,** *or*, THE CHILD'S FIRST BOOK.
Derby, Bemrose *c*1820

384 **An Early stage on the road to learning.** *illustrated* 1824

385 **Davies, T.** THE NEWEST READING MADE COMPLETELY EASY. *illustrated* Derby 1827

386 **Smith, J.** PRETTY STORIES WITH PRETTY PICTURES to instruct and amuse little folks. Dean & Munday *c*1830

387 **A New and easy introduction to arithmetic.**
J. Marshall 1800

388 **Marmaduke Multiply's merry method of making minor mathematicians.** Harris 1816

389 **Grandmamma Easy's merry multiplication.**
Dean & Son *c*1850

PRIMARY INSTRUCTION

390 **The Rational dame,** *or*, HINTS TOWARDS SUPPLYING PRATTLE FOR CHILDREN. *illustrated* J. Marshall 1790

391 **Instructive hints in easy lessons for children.** Part II. *illustrated* 1806

392 **Fenwick, Mrs.** RAYS OF THE RAINBOW : being an easy method for perfecting children in the first principles of grammar . . . 1812

393 **The Whim Wham,** *or,* EVENING AMUSEMENT FOR ALL AGES AND SIZES. Being an entire new set of riddles, charades, questions and transpositions. *frontispiece* 1816

394 **Clark, T.** THE ENGLISH MOTHER'S FIRST CATECHISM FOR HER CHILDREN. *illustrated* 1822

395 **Elliott, Mary.** PLAIN THINGS FOR LITTLE FOLKS ; seasoned with instruction both for the mind and the eye. *illustrated* 1823

396 **Fletcher, W.** THE PICTURESQUE PRIMER, *or,* useful matter made pleasing pastime for leisure hours. *illustrated* 1828

397 **The Little enquirer,** *or,* instructive conversations for children from five to six years of age. *illustrated* 1830

398 **Lovechild, Mrs.** INFANTILE KNOWLEDGE, a spelling and reading book. *illustrated.* 7th edition. *c*1840

399 **Corner, Miss.** THE PLAYGRAMMAR. 11th ed. *illustrated.* *c*1850

400 **Blair, David.** WHY AND BECAUSE, *or,* the curious child answered. 25th ed. *c*1870

RELIGIOUS INSTRUCTION

401 **Trimmer, Mrs.** A SERIES OF PRINTS OF SCRIPTURE HISTORY. 1786

402 **Trimmer, Mrs.** A NEW SERIES OF PRINTS . . . being an improved edition of the first set of scripture prints, from the Old Testament. J. Harris 1808

403 **Trimmer, Mrs.** A SERIES OF PRINTS DESIGNED TO ILLUSTRATE THE NEW TESTAMENT. 1828

404 **Fisher, James.** SCRIPTURE RIDDLES. *illustrated.* Derby 1823

405 **Scripture histories.** Decorated with cuts. Wellington *c*1830

406 **A Hieroglyphic Bible.** *illustrated* 1832

407 Another edition. *illustrated* 1838

The hieroglyphic Bible was a popular form of picture book for many years. It was first published about 1780. Some of the original woodcuts have been attributed to Bewick.

LAWS & CONSTITUTION

408 **Goldsmith, J.** A BRIEF GRAMMAR OF THE LAWS AND CONSTITUTION OF ENGLAND. *illustrated* Phillip 1809

409 **Taylor, Jeffery.** PARLOUR COMMENTARIES ON THE CONSTITUTION AND LAWS OF ENGLAND. *illustrated* Harris 1825

NATURAL SCIENCE

410 **A Description of a great variety of animals and vegetables** . . . being a supplement to three hundred animals. *illustrated* 1744

411 **A Description of three hundred animals.** A new edition. *illustrated* 1786

412 **A Concise abridgement of natural history in five volumes for the Juvenile or Child's Library.** Consisting of the following subjects : Quadrupeds, Birds, Fishes, Insects, Trees and Flowers. *illustrated* J. Marshall 1800

413 **A Good childs cabinet of natural history in four volumes.** *illustrated* J. Wallis 1801

414 **Smith, Thomas.** A COMPENDIOUS SYSTEM OF ASTRONOMY. 1806

415 **Telescope, Tom.** THE NEWTONIAN SYSTEM OF PHILOSOPHY. *illustrated* 1806

416 **The Young botanist,** *or,* THIRTEEN DIALOGUES. *illustrated* 1810

417 **A History of my pet animals during a year's residence in the country, addressed to my niece Selina.** *illustrated.* 2nd ed. *c*1830

418 **Wilson, T.** THE LITTLE CONCHOLOGIST. *illustrated. c*1830

419- **Tommy Trip's museum.** Parts I & II. *illustrated.* 1832
420

421 **Coloured Panoramic Alphabet of Natural History.** *c*1835

422 **Mary's scrap book.** *illustrated* 1838

423 **Uncle Philip's conversations with the children about tools and trades among inferior animals.** *illustrated* Leeds 1849

424 **Gardiner, William.** TWENTY LESSONS ON BRITISH MOSSES. 4th edition. 1852

425 **Bishop, James.** A VISIT TO THE ZOOLOGICAL GARDENS, in the Regent's Park. *illustrated c*1860

GARDENING

426 **Johns, C. A.** GARDENING FOR CHILDREN. *illustrated* 1848

427 **Birds and flowers,** *or,* THE CHILDREN'S GUIDE TO GARDENING AND BIRD KEEPING. *frontispiece* 1862

TRADE & COMMERCE

428- **The Book of trades.** 3 vols. *illustrated* 1806
430

31

431 **Mortimer, Thomas.** A GRAMMAR ILLUSTRATING THE PRIN-
CIPLES AND PRACTICE OF TRADE AND COMMERCE, for the use of
young persons intended for business. *frontispiece*   1810

432 **The Promised visit.** Including an account of the various
methods of manufacturing paper in different countries.
illustrated   1818

433 **Little Jack of all trades,** *or*, MECHANICAL ARTS DESCRIBED IN
PROSE AND VERSE SUITED TO THE CAPACITIES OF CHILDREN.
illustrated   1823

434 **Taylor, Isaac.** SCENES OF BRITISH WEALTH FOR THE AMUSEMENT
OF LITTLE TARRY-AT-HOME TRAVELLERS. *illustrated*   1823

ENGLAND & OTHER COUNTRIES

435 **The Travels of Tom Thumb over England and Wales.** 1746

436 **A Fortnight's tour through different parts of the country,**
by Master Tommy Newton, including original anecdotes
of several little misses and masters. Embellished with cuts.
F. Power 1790

437 **An Abridgement of geography adorned with cuts
representing the dress of each country.** J. Marshall 1800

438 **Captain Cook's voyage to the Pacific Ocean.** *illustrated*
J. Marshall 1800

439- **Copper plate views of interesting places in England.**
440   2 vols.   J. Marshall 1800

441- **Venning, Mary A. A Geographical present,** being des-
442   criptions of the principal countries of the world. 1st & 2nd
editions. *illustrated*   1817-1818

443 **City scenes,** *or*, A PEEP IN LONDON FOR CHILDREN. *illustrated*
1818

444- **Hack, Maria.** WINTER EVENINGS, *or*, tales of travellers. 4 vols.
447   *illustrated*   1818

448 **O'Keeffe, Miss.** NATIONAL CHARACTERS EXHIBITED IN FORTY
GEOGRAPHICAL POEMS. *with plates*   1818

449 **Thirty-two remarkable places in old England for the
instruction and entertainment of youth.** *illustrated*
1818

450 **The Traveller,** *or*, AN ENTERTAINING JOURNEY ROUND THE
HABITABLE GLOBE ; being a novel and easy method of studying
geography. *illustrated*   1820

451 **Taylor, Jane.** RURAL SCENES, *or*, a peep into the country for
children. *illustrated*   1826

452 **Aspin, J.** COSMORAMA ; a view of the costumes and peculiarities
of all nations. *illustrated*   1827

453 **The County album,** containing four hundred topographical hieroglyphics indicative of the products, staple commodities, manufactures, and objects of interest in England and Wales for the amusement and instruction of fireside tourists. 1829

454 **Holidays at Brighton,** *or,* SEASIDE AMUSEMENTS. *illustrated* 1834

455 **Tracings of maritime discovery.** *illustrated* 1841

456 **Mogridge, George.** LOITERINGS AMONG THE LAKES OF CUMBERLAND AND WESTMORELAND. *Baxter frontispiece* c1850

HISTORY

457 **Trimmer, Mrs.** Series of prints of English history designed as ornaments for those apartments in which children receive the first rudiments of their education. J. Marshall 1792

458 **Trimmer, Mrs.** A series of prints of Roman history. J. Marshall 1789

459 *also :* A New series of prints. 1804

460 **Trimmer, Mrs.** A series of prints of ancient history. J. Marshall 1786

461 **Cooper, Rev. M. L.** THE HISTORY OF NORTH AMERICA. *illustrated* E. Newbery 1789

462 **Trimmer, Mrs.** A new series of prints, accompanied by easy lessons : containing a general outline of Roman history. 1803

463- **Trimmer, Mrs.** A CONCISE HISTORY OF ENGLAND. 2 vols.
464 *illustrated* 1808

465 **Brown, Louisa.** HISTORICAL QUESTIONS ON THE KINGS OF ENGLAND. In verse. *illustrated* 1815

466 **More stories selected from the history of England for children.** *illustrated* 1821

467 **Sandham, E.** THE HISTORY OF ELIZABETH WOODVILLE. *illustrated* 1822

468- **Taylor, Jeffreys.** THE LITTLE HISTORIANS. 3 vols. *illustrated*
470 1824

BIOGRAPHY

471 **The Juvenile Plutarch :** containing accounts of the lives of children, and of the infancy of illustrious men who have been remarkable for their early progress in knowledge. *illustrated* 1801

472- *also* 4th edition. 2 vols. 1820
473

474 **Military heroes that have distinguished themselves during the late wars.** 1818

475- **Taylor, Isaac.** BEGINNINGS OF BIOGRAPHY. 2 vols. *illustrated*
476 1824

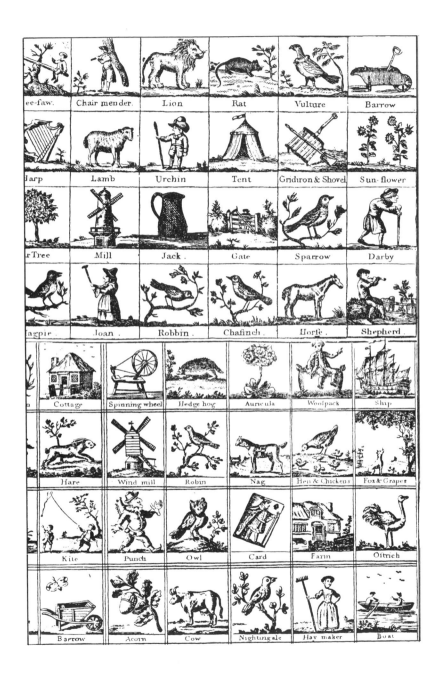

ee-faw.	Chair mender.	Lion	Rat	Vulture	Barrow
Harp	Lamb	Urchin	Tent	Gridiron & Shovel	Sun-flower
r Tree	Mill	Jack.	Gate	Sparrow	Darby
agpie.	Joan.	Robbin.	Chafinch.	Horfe.	Shepherd.
Cottage	Spinning wheel	Hedge hog	Auricula	Woolpack	Ship
Hare	Wind mill	Robin	Nag	Hen & Chickens	Fox & Grapes
Kite	Punch	Owl	Card	Farm	Oftrich
Barrow	Acorn	Cow	Nightingale	Hay maker	Boat